APR 11 '61	FEB 11		
MAY 3			
JAN 8			
APR 11			
OCT 9			
OCT 23			
JAN 5			
NOV 1			
FEB 27			
Baker			

5194

Teasdale, Sara

Stars tonight (poetry)

Stars To-Night

BOOKS BY SARA TEASDALE

Sonnets to Duse

Helen of Troy and Other Poems

Rivers to the Sea

Love Songs

Flame and Shadow

Dark of the Moon

Anthologies:

The Answering Voice: Love Lyrics by Women

Rainbow Gold: Poems Old and New, Selected for Boys and Girls

STARS TO-NIGHT

VERSES NEW AND OLD FOR BOYS AND GIRLS

By

SARA TEASDALE

Illustrated by Dorothy P. Lathrop

THE MACMILLAN COMPANY
NEW YORK

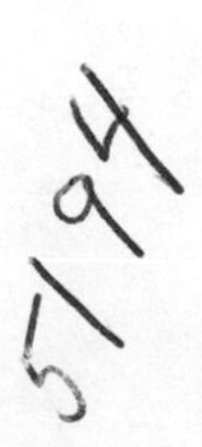

Eighteeth Printing, 1967

PRINTED IN THE UNITED STATES OF AMERICA

To Margaret Conklin

Thanks are due to the editors of Scribner's Magazine, The Yale Review, Ladies' Home Journal, Poetry and other publications for their permission to reprint certain of the following poems.

For permission to set any of the poems to music, application should be made to the publishers.

CONTENTS

CONTENTS

Stars To-Night

Night

Stars over snow,
 And in the west a planet
Swinging below a star—
 Look for a lovely thing and you will find it,
It is not far—
 It never will be far.

D.P.L

Stars

Alone in the night
  On a dark hill
With pines around me
  Spicy and still,

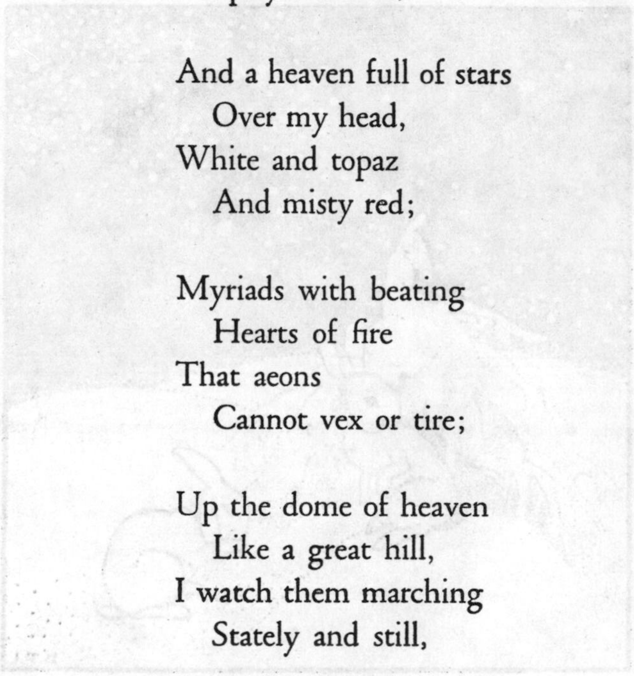

And a heaven full of stars
  Over my head,
White and topaz
  And misty red;

Myriads with beating
  Hearts of fire
That aeons
  Cannot vex or tire;

Up the dome of heaven
  Like a great hill,
I watch them marching
  Stately and still,

And I know that I
  Am honored to be
Witness
  Of so much majesty.

D.P. Lathrop

The Coin

Into my heart's treasury
  I slipped a coin
That time cannot take
  Nor a thief purloin,—
Oh, better than the minting
  Of a gold-crowned king
Is the safe-kept memory
  Of a lovely thing.

Late October

I found ten kinds of wild flowers growing
On a steely day that looked like snowing:
Queen Anne's lace, and blue heal-all,
A buttercup, straggling, grown too tall,
A rusty aster, a chicory flower—
Ten I found in half an hour.
The air was blurred with dry leaves flying,
Gold and scarlet, gaily dying.
A squirrel ran off with a nut in his mouth,
And always, always, flying south,
Twittering, the birds went by
Flickering sharp against the sky,
Some in great bows, some in wedges,
Some in bands with wavering edges;
Flocks and flocks were flying over
With the north wind for their drover.
"Flowers," I said, "you'd better go,
Surely it's coming on for snow,"—
They did not heed me, nor heed the birds,
Twittering thin, far-fallen words—
The others thought of to-morrow, but they
Only remembered yesterday.

D.P.L

The Cloud

I am a cloud in the heaven's height,
The stars are lit for my delight,
Tireless and changeful, swift and free,
I cast my shadow on hill and sea—
But why do the pines on the mountain's crest
Call to me always, "Rest, rest."

I throw my mantle over the moon
And I blind the sun on his throne at noon,
Nothing can tame me, nothing can bind,
I am a child of the heartless wind—
But oh, the pines on the mountain's crest
Whispering always, "Rest, rest."

The Sea Wind

I am a pool in a peaceful place,
I greet the great sky face to face,
I know the stars and the stately moon
And the wind that runs with rippling shoon—
But why does it always bring to me
The far-off, beautiful sound of the sea?

The marsh-grass weaves me a wall of green,
But the wind comes whispering in between,
In the dead of night when the sky is deep
The wind comes waking me out of sleep—
Why does it always bring to me
The far-off, terrible call of the sea?

"There Will Be Stars"

There will be stars over the place forever;
Though the house we loved and the street we loved are lost,
Every time the earth circles her orbit
On the night the autumn equinox is crossed,
Two stars we knew, poised on the peak of midnight
Will reach their zenith; stillness will be deep;
There will be stars over the place forever,
There will be stars forever, while we sleep.

February Twilight

I stood beside a hill
  Smooth with new-laid snow,
A single star looked out
  From the cold evening glow.

There was no other creature
  That saw what I could see—
I stood and watched the evening star
  As long as it watched me.

The Falling Star

I saw a star slide down the sky,
Blinding the north as it went by,
Too burning and too quick to hold,
Too lovely to be bought or sold,
Good only to make wishes on
And then forever to be gone.

D.P. Lathrop

The Spicebush in March

Spicebush, yellow spicebush, tell me
   Where you found so much clear gold?
Every branch and every twig
   Has as much as it can hold,
Flaunting before tattered winter
   Your new dress the wind whips round—
Color, color! You were first,
   You dredged and drew it from the ground!

Calm Morning at Sea

Midocean like a pale blue morning-glory
  Opened wide, wide;
The ship cut softly through the silken surface;
  We watched white sea-birds ride
Unrocking on the holy virgin water
  Fleckless on every side.

D.P.L

To Arcturus Returning

Arcturus, with the spring returning,
  I love you best; I cannot tell
Why, save that your recurrent burning
  Is spring's most punctual miracle.

You bring with you all longed-for things,
  Birds with their song, leaves with their stir,
And you, beyond all other stars,
  Have been man's comforter.

D.P. Lathrop

May Night

The spring is fresh and fearless
And every leaf is new,
The world is brimmed with moonlight,
The lilac brimmed with dew.

Here in the moving shadows
I catch my breath and sing—
My heart is fresh and fearless
And over-brimmed with spring.

A June Day

I heard a red-winged black-bird singing
    Down where the river sleeps in the reeds;
That was morning, and at noontime
    A humming-bird flashed on the jewel-weeds;
Clouds blew up, and in the evening
    A yellow sunset struck through the rain,
Then blue night, and the day was ended
    That never will come again.

Summer Evening

Evening, and all the birds
  In a chorus of shimmering sound
Are easing their hearts of joy
  For miles around.

The air is still and sweet,
  The few first stars are white,—
Oh let me like the birds
  Sing before night.

D.P.Lathrop-

On the Sussex Downs

Over the downs there were birds flying,
Far off glittered the sea,
And toward the north the weald of Sussex
Lay like a kingdom under me.

I was happier than the larks
That nest on the downs and sing to the sky,
Over the downs the birds flying
Were not so happy as I.

It was not you, though you were near,
Though you were good to hear and see,
It was not earth, it was not heaven
It was myself that sang in me.

Redbirds

Redbirds, redbirds,
Long and long ago,
What a honey-call you had
In hills I used to know;

Redbud, buckberry,
Wild plum-tree
And proud river sweeping
Southward to the sea,

Brown and gold in the sun
Sparkling far below,
Trailing stately round her bluffs
Where the poplars grow—

Redbirds, redbirds,
Are you singing still
As you sang one May day
On Saxton's Hill?

Full Moon: Santa Barbara

I listened, there was not a sound to hear
    In the great rain of moonlight pouring down,
The eucalyptus trees were carved in silver,
    And a light mist of silver lulled the town.

I saw far off the grey Pacific bearing
    A broad white disk of flame,
And on the garden-walk a snail beside me
    Tracing in crystal the slow way he came.

D.P.L.

Rhyme of November Stars

The noiseless marching of the stars
Sweeps above me all night long;
Up the skies, over the skies,
Passes the uncounted throng,
Without haste, without rest,
From the east to the west:
Vega, Deneb, white Altair
Shine like crystals in the air,
And the lonely Fomalhaut
In the dark south, paces low.
Now the timid Pleiades
Leave the shelter of the trees,
While toward the north, mounting high,
Gold Capella, like a queen,
Watches over her demesne
Stretching toward the kingly one,
Dusky, dark Aldebaran.
Betelguese and Rigel burn

D.P. Lathrop

In their wide wheel, slow to turn,
And in the sharp November frost
Bright Sirius, with his blue light
Completes the loveliness of night.

Winter Solstice

Dawn turned on her purple pillow
  And late, late came the winter day,
Snow was curved to the boughs of the willow,
  The sunless world was white and grey.

At noon we heard a blue-jay scolding,
  At five the last thin light was lost
From snow-banked windows faintly holding
  The feathery filigree of frost.

D.P.L.

I Stood Upon a Star

I stretched my mind until I stood
    Out in space, upon a star;
I looked, and saw the flying earth
    Where seven planets are.

Delicately interweaving
    Like fireflies on a moist June night,
The planetoids among the planets
    Played for their own delight.

I watched earth putting off her winter
    And slipping into green;
I saw the dark side of the moon
    No man has ever seen.

Like shining wheels in an opened watch
    They all revolved with soundless motion;
Earth sparkled like a rain-wet flower,
    Bearing her petals, plain and ocean.

D.P. Lathrop

The Fountain

All through the deep blue night
  The fountain sang alone;
It sang to the drowsy heart
  Of the satyr carved in stone.

The fountain sang and sang,
  But the satyr never stirred—
Only the great white moon
  In the empty heaven heard.

The fountain sang and sang
  While on the marble rim
The milk-white peacocks slept,
  And their dreams were strange and dim.

Bright dew was on the grass,
  And on the ilex, dew,
The dreamy milk-white birds
  Were all a-glisten, too.

The fountain sang and sang
  The things one cannot tell;
The dreaming peacocks stirred
  And the gleaming dew-drops fell.

Winter Noon

Snow-dust driven over the snow
    In glittering light,
Low hills, far as the eye can go,
    White on white;
Blue as a blue jay, shadows run
    Due north from every tree—
Chipmunk, do you like the sun,
    The blowing snow and me?

D.P.L.

The Faëry Forest

The faëry forest glimmered
  Beneath an ivory moon,
The silver grasses shimmered
  Against a faëry tune.

Beneath the silken silence
  The crystal branches slept,
And dreaming through the dew-fall
  The cold, white blossoms wept.

D.P.Lathrop

Autumn Dusk

I saw above a sea of hills
  A solitary planet shine,
And there was no one near or far
  To keep the world from being mine.